Angels Are My Friends

Angels Are My Friends

By Annetta E. Dellinger   Illustrated by Arthur W. Kirchoff

CONCORDIA®

Publishing House
St. Louis

Unless otherwise noted, the Scripture quotations in this publication are from The Holy Bible: NEW INTERNATIONAL VERSION. Copyright © 1978 by the International Bible Society. Used by permission of Zondervan Bible Publishers.

"A Morning Prayer" is from *Lutheran Worship*, "Responsive Prayer 1," copyright © 1982 by Concordia Publishing House, St. Louis.

Copyright © 1985 Concordia Publishing House
3558 S. Jefferson Avenue, St. Louis, MO 63118-3968
Manufactured in the United States of America

All rights reserved. No part of this publication may be reproduced, stored in a retrieval system, or transmitted, in any form or by any means, electronic, mechanical, photocopying, recording, or otherwise, without the prior written permission of Concordia Publishing House.

Library of Congress Cataloging in Publication Data

Dellinger, Annetta E.
  Angels are my friends.

  Summary: A grandmother uses Bible passages to explain the nature of angels to her young grand-daughter.
  1. Angels—Biblical teaching—Juvenile literature.
[1. Angels] I. Title.
BS680.A48D45   1985   235'.3   85-7858
ISBN 0-570-04120-1

    2   3   4   5   6   7   8   9   10   DP   94

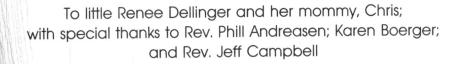

To little Renee Dellinger and her mommy, Chris;
with special thanks to Rev. Phill Andreasen; Karen Boerger;
and Rev. Jeff Campbell

A Morning Prayer

We give thanks to you, heavenly Father, through
Jesus Christ your dear Son, that you have protected us
through the night from all danger and harm. We ask
you to preserve and keep us, this day also, from all sin
and evil that in all our thoughts, words and deeds we
may serve and please you. Into your hands we
commend our bodies and souls and all that is ours. Let
your holy angels have charge of us that the wicked
one have no power over us. Amen.

"She's here! She's here!" Renee shouted as she ran to open the door. "I'm glad to see you, Grammy. I've been waiting all day. I didn't think you would ever get here."

"I'm glad to see you, too," Grandmother said as she gave Renee a big, big hug. "And here's the surprise I promised to bring you. It was mine when I was a little girl, but now I want to give it to you."

Renee was very excited. She loved presents, especially the ones her grandmother gave her. Renee hurriedly slipped off the bow, took the lid off the box, and gently lifted the edges of the bright yellow tissue paper.

As Renee lifted out a picture of an angel, she giggled, "Thank you! Let's go set it on the table next to my bed." Renee grabbed Grandmother's hand to pull her toward the bedroom. "I love having a picture of an angel. What's his name?"

After a moment's pause, Renee asked a whole bunch of questions. "Grammy, do you know what angels *really* are? What do they do? What are they like? Do they all look like this one? Have you ever seen one?"

"Oh, my," Grammy laughed as she shook her head. "I think we better sit down."

Grandmother sat down in the big old rocking chair next to Renee's bed and lifted her onto her lap. Then Grammy took a little red Bible out of her purse.

"I know what that is," Renee said. "It's a Bible. And every word in it is true because it is God's Word"

(John 17:17).

"You are exactly right," Grammy said with a smile as they cuddled close together. "The Bible is where we will find the answers to your questions about angels."

Together Renee and Grammy looked up the Bible passages.

"Long, long ago," Grammy said, "God made the world out of nothing. He made the heavens and earth and everything. When He was finished, He looked at everything and said it was good *(Genesis 1:31)*. And that includes all the angels," Grammy added *(Colossians 1:16)*.

"Where do they live?" Renee asked. "In church?"

"Angels live with God in heaven and praise Him," Grandmother replied. "Their main job is to serve Him and to do whatever He tells them to do. The angels love God very much and would never do anything that would make Him unhappy" *(Psalm 103:20–21)*.

Renee looked at her new picture of the one angel and then at Grandmother. "You mean, this isn't the only angel?"

"Oh, no," said Grammy. "The Bible tells us that God made thousands and thousands of angels *(Revelation 5:11)*. Remember the Christmas story? 'Suddenly a great company of the heavenly host'—that means angels—'appeared with the angel praising God' *(Luke 2:13)*. The words a great company mean a great many—more than you or I could ever count. The exact number doesn't matter because God has made enough angels to do everything He wants."

"How does God remember all those angels?" Renee asked. "Do they all look different?"

"I don't know," said Grandmother. "God made *people* to look just the way He wanted them, and He made the *angels* also just the way He wanted. But the Bible doesn't tell us very much about their looks. Actually, God made angels invisible; so people can't usually see them. The picture is only one artist's idea of what he thought an angel might look like. And that's what all pictures of angels are—just somebody's idea.

"Angels are spirits; that's why we can't see them. But they are not 'bad ghosts.' God's angels are good, and they help us. So we never have to be afraid of them *(Luke 2:10)*. And since they love God, they love us, too.

"Sometimes, though, God has a special job for an angel to do, and He allows a person to see the angel. The night Jesus was born, a bright light shone around the shepherds, and they saw an angel in the light.

"Another time, God and two angels visited Abraham, and they looked like men" *(Genesis 18:2; 19:1)*.

"Sometimes they look like fire. Ezekiel, a prophet in the Bible, wrote, 'The appearance of the living creatures'—that's angels again—'was like burning coals of fire or like torches' *(Ezekiel 1:13)*.

"I suppose," Grandmother continued, "they can look like anything God wants them to look like when He lets people see them. But whatever they look like, they won't hurt God's people. Instead, they help us *(Hebrews 1:14)*.

"Angels are very wise," Grandmother added. "They are more wise than the wisest man in the whole world—but they do not know as much as God, because God knows all things *(Matthew 24:36)*.

"Angels are also stronger than the strongest person on earth, but they are not as strong as God, for only 'with God all things are possible' (Mark 10:27 KJV). Remember the angel that rolled back the giant stone in front of Jesus' tomb on Easter Morning (Matthew 28:2)? It took many men to put that stone there."

"Wow!" said Renee. "Angels sound *almost* as strong as God."

"Ah," said Grandmother, "but they aren't. For example, angels can only be in one place at a time, but God can be everywhere at all times (Matthew 28:20). Angels are fast, though. They can move faster than a rocket (Ezekiel 1:14). They can be here one second and somewhere else the next."

"Is that because they have wings, Grammy?"

"Well," said Grandmother, "some have wings. But the Bible tells us about several kinds of angels. One kind, the *seraphim*, do have wings—six of them *(Isaiah 6:2–3)*. They praise and worship God. The *cherubim* are very beautiful angels *(Revelation 4:3)*. Some of them were God's special guards at the Garden of Eden" *(Genesis 3:24)*.

Renee kept staring at her picture of the angel. She wondered if *any* angel looked exactly like this one. Grammy said, "Don't fret about what they look like. Think about what they *do*—and thank God for that.

"God often used His angels to give messages to people. The word *angel* means "messenger." Gabriel was a special messenger of God. He brought messages of good news to the people on earth. Do you remember which angel spoke to Zechariah and to Mary before Jesus was born?"

"Was it Gabriel?" Renee guessed.

"Yes," said Grandmother. "That's who it was *(Luke 1:19, 26–27)*. Now—Gabriel himself might never talk to you, Renee, but God does use His angels to take care of you and to protect you in many ways—even in ways you can't see. God says in Psalm 91, verse 11, 'He will command His angels concerning you to guard you in all your ways.' God does that because He loves you *(John 3:16)*.

"Do you know that God sends His angels to care for you at home and at school and at church and in the car and at the park and in the day and in the night and when you are in bed and everywhere?" (Grandmother took a deep breath after so long a sentence.)

"Renee, when you are afraid or feel alone, God's angels are with you, protecting and helping you. People sometimes forget that God's angels are with them. But whether they remember or not, God says, 'The angels of the Lord encamp around those who fear him, and he delivers them'" *(Psalm 34:7)*.

As Grandmother closed her Bible, she added, "Of course, even though angels are wonderful and we thank God for our good angel friends, we should never worship or pray to them. We worship and pray to God alone" *(Matthew 4:10)*.

Renee said, "I'm so glad God made angels! Now I know a lot about them. But won't I *ever* see one?"

"You will when you get to heaven," Grammy answered. "Everyone who believes in Jesus will see them then. Won't that be wonderful" *(Matthew 25:31)*.

Renee was quiet for a little while as Grammy held her tightly and rocked back and forth in the squeeky old chair. Then Renee quietly asked, "Grammy, do angels just take care of little children?"

"Oh, no," Grammy quickly replied. "Everyone who loves God is His child—no matter how young or old. And because God never stops loving His children, He never takes away His angels—certainly not because the children grow up" (Psalm 91:11).

"Grammy, I'm glad you gave me this picture of an angel," Renee sighed. Then she gave Grammy a big, big hug and smiled, "I'm glad God made angels and that angels are my friends."